Reflection and Reflective Practice

Production

Reflection and Reflective Practice cover, book design
and implementation by Christopher Wilson at Oberphones
Illustrations by Jo @ Kja-artists
Printed in the UK by CLOC

City & Guilds

1 Giltspur Street
London EC1A 9DD
T +44 (0)844 543 0000
publishingfeedback@cityandguilds.com
www.cityandguilds.com

Contents

Introduction

The idea of this Pocket Guide is to provide a quick and easy reference guide for care staff. The book is structured around three core questions:

▶ **WHAT** is reflective practice?
▶ **WHY** is reflective practice important in social care?
▶ **HOW** can social care workers apply and use reflective practice?

The standards of current qualifications in care have been carefully considered in writing this Pocket Guide.

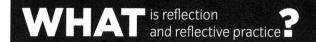
WHAT is reflection and reflective practice?

Smith and Karban (2006:4) argue that reflective practice is 'accepted as being a key component of practice in health and social care'. However, there is no clear single understanding of what is meant by reflective practice in social care. This section in the Pocket Guide therefore considers the following questions:

▶   **What is reflection?**
▶   **What is reflective practice?**
▶   **What are the different forms of reflective practice?**
▶   **What models of reflective practice are most used in social care?**
▶   **What are the attributes of a reflective practitioner?**

DEFINING REFLECTION

The mental process of trying to structure or restructure an experience, a problem or existing knowledge or insights.

Korthagen 2001:58

A process of reviewing an experience of practice in order to describe, analyse, evaluate and so inform learning about practice.

Reid 1993:305

Active, persistent and careful consideration of any belief or supposed form of knowledge in the light of the grounds that support it and the further conclusions to which it tends.

Dewey 1933:118

A reflection in a mirror is an exact replica of what is in front of it. Reflection in professional practice, however, gives back not what it is but what it might be, an improvement on the original.

Biggs 1999:6

DEFINING REFLECTIVE PRACTICE

Something more than thoughtful practice. It is that form of practice that seeks to problematise many situations of professional performance so that they can become potential learning situations and so the practitioner can continue to learn, grow and develop in and through practice.

Jarvis 1992:180

In its broadest sense, reflective practice involves the critical analysis of everyday working practices to improve competence and promote professional development.

Clouder 2000

A set of abilities and skills, to indicate the taking of a critical stance, an orientation to problem solving or state of mind.

Moon 1999:63

DIFFERENT FORMS OF REFLECTION

Perhaps the most well-known writing about reflective practice comes from **Donald Schön**, whose book *The Reflective Practitioner* (1983) is generally seen as the most influential work on the subject. Essentially, Schön proposed two very different (but potentially linked) forms of reflection:

REFLECTION IN ACTION   **REFLECTION ON ACTION**

Many writers and researchers have commented on and further developed Schön's work. **Killian and Todnem** (1991) extended Schön's ideas by proposing a third type of reflection:

REFLECTION FOR ACTION

REFLECTION IN ACTION

Essentially, this is about reflecting in the present – while we are actually 'doing' something. It is often referred to as 'thinking on our feet'. In many ways this is simply good practice, as it means thinking about what you are doing while you are doing it, rather than letting your mind wander off elsewhere. It sounds simple and of course we all think we do it all the time, but how often do care staff talk to their colleagues about what they are having for tea, where they went on holiday, etc rather than focusing purely on the task at hand?

The practitioner allows himself to experience surprise, puzzlement or confusion in a situation which he finds uncertain or unique. He reflects on the phenomenon before him and on the prior understandings which have been implicit in his behaviour. He carries out an experiment which serves to generate both a new understanding of the phenomenon and a change in the situation.

Schön 1983:68

Reflection in action involves a practitioner focusing on the task at hand and:

THINKING AHEAD	BEING CRITICAL	STORING UP EXPERIENCES FOR THE FUTURE	ANALYSING WHAT IS HAPPENING
('Right, if that has happened, then I need to …')	('That didn't work very well; I'd better try …')	('I could have dealt with that better; if she says it again, I will …') This might also be about identifying issues for reflection at a later stage.	('He is doing that to test me; I think I should respond by …')

Schön's distinction between the two types of reflection has been the focus of considerable debate. A number of writers claim that Schön's reflection in action does not actually constitute reflection. For example, **Eraut** (1994:145) states that 'when time is extremely short, decisions have to be rapid and the space for reflection is extremely limited'. The argument is that reflection in action is nothing more than what might be called thoughtful or mindful practice.

Certainly, there are disadvantages to reflection in action:

▶   You can only see things from your own perspective ('I think…'; 'I feel…'; 'I'm not sure…')

▶   The reflection will only ever be short term (and therefore it will only ever look at the 'surface') because if your mind is on the task at hand, when the task changes, so will the reflection

REFLECTION ON ACTION

This is separate to, but linked with, reflection in action. It is the reflection done later, after the event (ie thinking about what you have done and why you did it that way at the end of a working day, talking to colleagues about your working practices, talking things through in supervision or writing something reflective about your work). It is in making the distinction between thinking 'on the job' and this later reflection that Schön's work has been so significant.

Reflection on action is free from the urgency and any pressures of the actual event. As such, it allows for longer-term reflection and addresses the drawbacks of reflection in action. For example, reflection on action allows for the opportunity to explore other people's views on the event. Feedback from others, therefore, adds an extra dimension to the reflection, allowing for more depth. You don't have to rely just on your opinion about the work you did – you can ask others what they think about it.

Reflection on action requires space and time and this is perhaps one of the most significant challenges for busy social care workers. One of the main drawbacks of reflection on action is that, because of time constraints, care staff tend only to think in this way about more complex or critical work issues. In terms of more routine events and work practice, there is a tendency only to reflect in action. This can mean that people do not make many changes to routine work practice. It is therefore important to plan in reflection on action to ensure that it covers every aspect of practice. This is why many organisations arrange staff meetings to discuss practice and changes to practice, as this allows the space for reflection on action. Supervision should also afford workers the time to discuss their reflections on their work.

REFLECTION FOR ACTION

Added later by **Killian and Todnem** (1991), reflection for action describes the stage of reflection where future actions are considered and perhaps planned for. As such, reflection for action serves to guide future work. Is it essentially reflection before an event.

BEFORE	▶	**DURING**	▶	**AFTER**
Reflection for action		Reflection in action		Reflection on action

When writing about reflective practice for teachers, **Reagan, Case and Brubacher** (2000) assert that reflective practice includes what the teacher does in preparation for class (reflection for action), what they do in class (reflection in action) and what they do after leaving class (reflection on action).

Therefore, in relation to a social care worker's practice, we could consider the three forms of reflection in terms of:

Reflection for action	Planning for the work to be carried out
Reflection in action	Reflecting as the work is actually taking place
Reflection on action	Thinking things through after the work, perhaps talking it over with colleagues or discussing it in supervision

Added together, the three forms of reflection should lead to an **action plan** for taking further action (thus taking us into reflection for action again).

Reflection on action should lead to further reflection for action in terms of planning what to do next. Essentially, a reflective cycle is produced, in which a truly reflective practitioner will be reflecting all the time, at different stages.

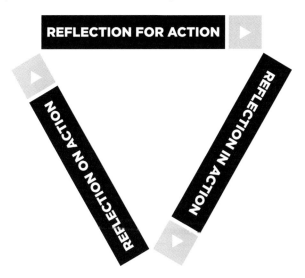

Greenaway (1995) explores this idea by creating a basic framework for reflection consisting of three stages and often depicted as a cycle in the following way:

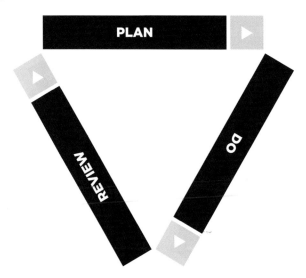

REFLECTION AND REFLECTIVE PRACTICE

MODELS OF REFLECTIVE PRACTICE

Various models of reflective practice have been developed since Schön first wrote about the process of reflection. The majority of these come from the health or education sectors, but they have much to offer social care as the sector develops its professional status. As social care becomes more established and develops a reflective approach more fully, it is likely that models specifically drawn out of this sector will develop.

Having a good grasp of the concepts of reflection in, on and for action is important in understanding the various models of reflective practice which have been developed. Some models provide a process for reflective practice and are better suited to reflecting either after or before an event (reflection on action or reflection for action). Other models, however, do not propose a process but refer to the skills, attributes and qualities needed for reflective practice, which means they can be used in any of the stages of reflective practice.

Using a particular model of reflective practice can help practitioners to become more reflective. However, which model people use is not important. What is important is that each social care worker finds a model of reflective practice with which they feel comfortable. In many ways the models provide a structure for thinking through the work that people undertake, and different people find different models useful.

The next few pages of this Pocket Guide will outline some of the models of reflective practice most widely used in social care.

JOHNS

This model (2000), which was developed in nursing, is popular in social care because of its focus on outcomes and improving practice. The idea of this model is that when you consider what you did (description of events), you reflect on what influenced the situation, focusing on three main areas:

▶ **Internal factors**: for example, how did I have an impact on this?
▶ **External factors**: for example, how did others have an impact on this? Or how did the environment affect it?
▶ **Knowledge**: for example, what knowledge did I use? Was it helpful?

Based on this reflection, you then think about what you might have done differently (could your practice have been better?), carefully considering what other choices you had (eg could you have used different knowledge? Could the environment have been improved?).

BOUD, KEOGH AND WALKER

According to this 1985 model, when being reflective, individuals:

▶ Recapture their experiences
▶ Mull them over (perhaps with others)
▶ Consider their feelings about the experiences (both positive and negative feelings)
▶ Evaluate the experiences – identifying new knowledge
▶ Act on the reflection – incorporating new knowledge into their planning

The consideration given to 'attending to feelings' in this model gives it a real strength for social care work, where feelings are so important in terms of practice.

EXPERIENCE(S)	REFLECTIVE PROCESS	OUTCOMES
▶ Behaviour ▶ Ideas ▶ Feelings	▶ Returning to the experience ▶ Utilising positive feelings ▶ Removing obstructing feelings ▶ Re-evaluating the experience	▶ New perspective on experience ▶ Change in behaviour ▶ Readiness for application ▶ Commitment to action

GIBBS

Gibbs (1988) developed six stages to reflective practice, which make up a continuous cycle. In common with Boud, Keogh and Walker, Gibbs encourages the practitioner to take feelings and emotions into account when reflecting on a situation, so this is a popular model in social care.

Stage 1: Description – describing factually what happened. *What happened? Who did what? What were the results?*

Stage 2: Feelings and thoughts – reflecting on what you were thinking and feeling at the time. *How were you feeling when the event began? How did your feelings change as the event unfolded? How did you feel about the outcomes? How do you feel about it now?*

Stage 3: Evaluation – thinking about what was good and what was bad about the experience, perhaps listing the positive and negative points. *What went well? What didn't go so well?*

Stage 4: Analysis – this develops on from Stage 3, but involves breaking the event down into component parts so that they can be explored separately. It involves considering more detailed questions than those covered in Stage 3. For example, 'What went well?' could be followed up with *What did I do well? What did others do well?* And 'What didn't go so well?' could be followed up with *What didn't turn out like it should have? In what way did I contribute to this? In what ways did others contribute to this?*

Stage 5: Conclusion – now that the event has been explored from a range of perspectives, the person reflecting should be able to draw some conclusions. This will involve asking *What could I have done differently? What impact would this have had on the outcome?* If the previous stages have not been fully and honestly explored then the conclusions reached in this stage will be fundamentally flawed.

Stage 6: Action planning – this stage entails looking at what you might do differently if a similar situation arose again.

BORTON

Developed in 1970, this model involves the following questions forming the framework for reflection:

This model is often criticised on the basis of its simplicity. However, it can be useful for more experienced practitioners who are confident about reflection and who do not want or need a highly structured framework.

WHAT?	▶	SO WHAT?	▶	NOW WHAT?
▶ What happened? ▶ What did I do? ▶ What did others do? ▶ What was I trying to achieve? ▶ What was actually achieved?		▶ So what is the importance of this? ▶ So what more do I need to know? ▶ So what have I learnt?		▶ Now what do I need to do? ▶ Now what different options have I got? ▶ Now what will be the consequences?

JAN FOOK

Jan Fook is perhaps the most well known contemporary writer on reflective practice in social work. Fook's writing on reflective practice emphasises the importance of the practitioner reflecting on power dynamics and exploring the implications of these in practice. This is what sets Fook's ideas apart from the many other models of reflective practice drawn from other professional backgrounds. This is particularly fitting, as an understanding of power dynamics and the impact that these have on people's lives is arguably one of the things that sets social care work as a profession apart from others.

Fook (2002) describes her model of critical reflection as an inductive process in which the workers develop their own theory of practice from the particular piece of practice and situation. Some social care workers find Fook's model problematic because of some of the words she uses. However, it is a very useful model and it is worth exploring it. The model is based on a three-stage process, which can be explained as follows:

TELLING THE NARRATIVE	▷	DECON-STRUCTING	▷	RECON-STRUCTING
This means describing the situation or 'telling the story'		This means taking the situation 'apart' to examine it. Fook suggests thinking about power carefully in this stage.		This means putting things back together – with a new understanding of the situation

SMYTH

This 1989 model for reflective practice in education brings together components of some of the models already covered:

Describe	What did I do?
Inform (analysis)	What does this mean?
Confront (explore)	How did I come to be like this and act like this?
Reconstruct (evaluate and change)	What does my work say about my assumptions, values and beliefs? Where did these ideas come from? What social practices are expressed in these ideas? Whose interests are served by my actions and my practice?

RAYNER

This model is still being developed. Written by social worker Rachel Rayner, it could be used to encourage others to reflect. It focuses on enabling practitioners to become more emotionally aware through their reflection.

▶ **Hair-raising moment**: where something amazing and unexpected happens, in a good way. Was there anything that took you by surprise or that you had not expected?

▶ **Heart-warming moment**: where you feel a sense of doing something competently. What were the moments that you thought went well? What made you feel good?

▶ **Tummy-sinking moment**: where you realise you could have done something differently for a better outcome. What did not go well? What would you change next time?

▶ **Toe-curling moment**: where something made you feel uncomfortable. Was there anything that made your 'toes curl'? What have you learned?

SURPRISES TO LEARNING

In 2000 the **University of York** developed the collaborative model of direct observation for social work students on placement. This contains guidance on the provision of feedback after the observation and provides the following subheadings to structure discussion about the observation:

- *Surprises*
- *Satisfactions*
- *Dissatisfactions*
- *Learning*

These headings can be used to provide the basis of reflective practice. For example, when reflecting back on a situation, it is useful to consider:

> *What surprised me about the event?*
> *What was I satisfied with?*
> *What was I dissatisfied about?*
> *What have I learnt?*

KORTHAGEN

This model (2001) refers to teachers but can easily be adapted to social care practice. The idea is that the practitioner reflects on a number of areas (represented as the layers of an 'onion'). The reflection becomes deeper as each layer is considered.

1 Environment – *what impact does the environment have on the situation?*
2 Behaviour – *what am I doing and what are others doing?*
3 Competences – *how effective is my practice? How competent am I? And how competent are others?*
4 Beliefs – *what is the impact of my beliefs and values (and those of others)?*
5 Identity – *how does my identity and that of others involved impact on the situation?*
6 Mission – *what is the purpose of my work? What is the reason I am here? Am I achieving this?*

REFLECTION AS A PROCESS: TRANSFORMATIVE LEARNING

In his later work, **Mezirow** (2000) suggests that there are 10 steps to transformative learning:

1   The practitioner has an experience that disorientates them
2   They examine themselves, exploring their personal thoughts and beliefs
3   They conduct a deep assessment of their assumptions and the alienation created by the challenge of these assumptions
4   They share and analyse their personal discontent and similar experiences with others
5   They explore various options for new ways of acting
6   They begin to develop confidence about new experiences and competence in new roles
7   They plan a course of action
8   They acquire the knowledge and develop the skills required for the action to be undertaken

| 9 | They try out the new behaviours and new skills, and seek and use feedback |
| 10 | They reintegrate with their new perspectives on life |

REFLECTION AND REFLECTIVE PRACTICE

CHARACTERISTICS AND ATTRIBUTES OF A REFLECTIVE PRACTITIONER

Brookfield (1988) asserts that the ability to engage in four activities is essential for a reflective practitioner:

- ▶ **Assumption analysis** – this involves thinking in a way which challenges our own beliefs and values. In doing so, we need to assess the impact of our assumptions on our way of seeing reality and on our daily functioning
- ▶ **Contextual awareness** – this is where we recognise that our views and assumptions are socially constructed in a specific cultural context
- ▶ **Imaginative speculation** – this is when we imagine different ways of thinking about something to provide us with the chance to challenge our way of doing things
- ▶ **Reflective scepticism** – this entails questioning 'truths'. It involves thinking about a subject in a completely new way, suspending any prior knowledge and beliefs

Roth (1989) summarised the basic elements of reflective practice as:

- Keeping an open mind about what, why and how we do things
- Awareness of what, why and how we do things
- Questioning what, why and how we do things
- Asking what, why and how other people do things
- Generating choices, options and possibilities
- Comparing and contrasting results
- Seeking to understand underlying mechanisms and rationales
- Viewing our activities and results from various perspectives
- Asking, 'What if?'
- Seeking feedback and other people's ideas and viewpoints

SUMMARISING REFLECTIVE PRACTICE

Reflective practice is about:

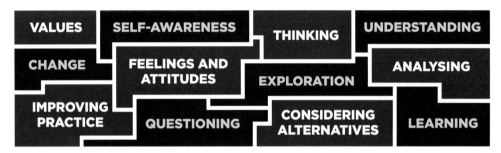

WHY is reflective practice important in social care **?**

To consider why reflective practice is so important in social care and why social care workers can find reflective practice challenging, this section explores:

▶   **Professionalism and reflection**
▶   **Learning and reflection**
▶   **Improving practice through reflection**
▶   **Ethics and reflective practice**
▶   **Emotional intelligence and reflective practice**
▶   **The barriers to reflective practice**

WHY IS REFLECTIVE PRACTICE IMPORTANT IN SOCIAL CARE?

It is generally agreed that reflective practice is important in social care because:

▶   It can lead to better practice and improved outcomes for service users

▶   Service users deserve to work with practitioners who recognise the vital importance of the work they do and who make the time to reflect on this

▶   It is a key aspect of professionalism

▶   It is closely linked with learning and thus can enhance professional development

▶   It can help practitioners to develop their practice wisdom, which is essential in social care work

▶   It improves accountability

▶   It helps practitioners to explore the basic assumptions underpinning their work and therefore helps to ensure ethical practice

- The skills and qualities required for reflective practice are very similar to the skills and qualities that are needed for best practice in social care work
- Reflection is important to everyone. The value of encouraging service users to reflect is becoming more widely recognised. It is therefore vital that social care workers understand reflective practice fully
- Social care workers who have developed their reflective practice skills report feeling empowered and an increased job satisfaction – see, for example, **Cosh** (2011)

PROFESSIONALISM AND REFLECTION

The **ACCESS** model of professionalism, as described by **Dean** (1995), demonstrates how reflection and professionalism are closely linked.

A *autonomy linked with accountability*: professionals have a level of autonomy which means that they do not need direction for every action they take. They do, however, need to be accountable for the decisions they make and the actions they take

C *commitment*: professionals have a level of commitment to their work – Dean describes the way a professional should have an allegiance to the client and the profession

C *collegiate*: essentially, this means that there should be a group identity within the profession

E *education*: a profession has an agreed body of knowledge which is passed on through extensive education

S   ***service-user driven***: *a professional is service-user-centred rather than focused on themselves. Professional standards expressed in statements such as codes of ethics set behavioural standards to maintain the user focus*

S   ***skills***: *a professional has specialist skills and takes an interest in expanding their skills to ensure that they are up to date and fit for purpose. A professional also takes an interest in expanding the knowledge and skills within the profession generally, assuming that professional practice can always be further developed*

It could be argued that it would be impossible for someone to meet the six components of professionalism outlined in Dean's model without being reflective.

LEARNING AND REFLECTION

Reflection and learning are closely linked in many ways. The models of reflective practice covered earlier in this Pocket Guide demonstrate this to some extent, whilst the majority of adult learning theories also illustrate the importance of reflection for learning.

The links between reflection and learning are clearly identified in **Kolb**'s (1984) experiential learning cycle. Kolb discusses how an individual goes from being an active participant in an experience, to reflecting on that experience, to analysing the experience and, finally, drawing conclusions with which to experiment in the future. As far as Kolb is concerned, an individual will not learn from an experience unless they reflect on that experience and move through the cycle of learning, as illustrated

I have an experience

CONCRETE EXPERIENCE

REFLECTIVE OBSERVATION

I reflect on the experience

I test out my conclusions and experiment with different behaviours

ACTIVE EXPERIMENT-ATION

ABSTRACT CONCEPTUAL-ISATION

I start to make links with other experiences and wider knowledge. I reach some conclusions about what I have learnt

LEARNING STYLES

Honey and Mumford (1982) report that people have different styles of learning. They developed four different styles and designed a questionnaire to identify which style a person uses. It is important to remember that people can display the characteristics of more than one style, but the theory is that most people have a dominant style for the way they learn. The styles can be linked closely with Kolb's learning cycle and an understanding of the way these connect can help when trying to understand why some people find it more difficult to reflect than others.

The four styles identified by Honey and Mumford are:

ACTIVISTS	**REFLECTORS**
THEORISTS	**PRAGMATISTS**

ACTIVISTS

Activists tend to be open-minded and enthusiastic. They like new experiences and want to get involved in the here and now. They enjoy 'getting stuck into' something and learn by doing. Activists can become bored when an activity stops and will want to move quickly on to the next challenge or activity rather than dwelling on what they have just been doing.

REFLECTORS

Reflectors do just what it says on the tin! They stand back, reflect, ponder and consider many perspectives before acting. Reflectors need to mull things over to feel comfortable in reaching a conclusion. They observe, gather information and use plenty of time to reach a decision.

THEORISTS

Theorists are logical thinkers. They analyse, question and learn step by step in a logical way. Theorists question any new learning: they want to make sure that they fully understand it and that it fits and makes sense with their logical approach. Theorists are often perfectionists and don't appreciate flippant approaches to a subject.

PRAGMATISTS

Pragmatists like to try new things out to see if they work in practice. They are essentially experimenters. They will often take a problem-solving approach to learning and will seek to apply something that they have learnt straight away. However, if their experiment doesn't work they are unlikely to try the approach again – they will look for something else to try out instead.

SURFACE AND DEEP APPROACHES TO LEARNING

First identified by **Marton and Saljo** (1976), the concept of deeper learning is closely linked to reflective practice, so it is important to have an understanding of these styles of learning.

A surface approach to learning focuses on acquiring and memorising information. An uncritical, unquestioning approach is taken to acquiring new knowledge and there is very little reflection. Learning is motivated by external factors such as demands from employers or assessment criteria.

A deep approach to learning involves critically analysing new ideas and linking them with existing knowledge. This approach means that learners will understand the information they acquire and will be able to apply their knowledge to new and different situations. Reflective practice is all about taking a deeper approach to learning; in fact, it is about taking a deeper approach to practice in general.

IMPROVING PRACTICE

Reflective practice improves social care practice in a range of ways. Perhaps most importantly, reflective practice opens up options; when we reflect on a situation, it enables us both to see more and to see things differently. Effectively, it 'illuminates our practice' so that we can see things more clearly. This can lead to more creative practice, which is important in the current climate and seemingly ever decreasing resources. **Brown and Rutter** (2006:41) claim that:

Reflecting [...] helps you to deliver good practice, as you become more able to develop and articulate the resources and services for your service users and be accountable for them.

Bolton (2001) asserts that reflective practice improves practice as it:

- *Helps practitioners to identify gaps in their skills and knowledge. This makes it easier for them to identify their learning needs and improve their practice*
- *Encourages practitioners to analyse communication and relationships. This means that relationships can be improved and therefore collaborative working is improved too*
- *Supports practitioners in examining the decision-making process, which can help them to justify practice*
- *Encourages a healthy questioning approach which can help practitioners to 'find their way'*

KNOWLEDGE, SKILLS AND VALUES

Effective social care practice is made up of knowledge, skills and values, as recognised in current social care qualifications. Many social care workers believe that the best way to extend their knowledge and to improve their skills is to go on training. However, as we have seen, reflection improves practice, in relation to knowledge, skills and values:

► Reflection can help practitioners to identify gaps in and extend their knowledge. It can also assist in making links so that people can develop ideas about how to use their existing knowledge in new situations

► Reflection can help aid skill development; when you reflect on how you handled a situation and think about the feedback you have had, it can help to develop skills further

► Reflecting on values can help practitioners to be more aware of their values and can assist in dealing with value conflicts

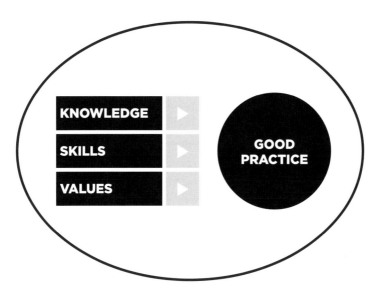

**KNOWLEDGE, SKILLS AND VALUES
ARE ENHANCED THROUGH REFLECTION**

PRACTICE WISDOM

Practice wisdom is a phrase often used to describe the knowledge which practitioners develop from their practice. Practitioners need to develop their knowledge, based on their practice experiences.

Hooper and Parrot (2006) say that professional knowledge extends beyond simply mechanistic views of what is 'known'; it stretches to what is often referred to as 'practice wisdom'. This means that professional knowledge involves some form of intuition, artistry or what can be referred to as 'inexpressible knowings'. This kind of professional artistry develops over time as each new professional extends the knowledge they gained through qualification by testing it out in their practice and reflecting on the experience. The development of this professional artistry is only possible where a practitioner is reflective about their practice.

SERVICE IMPROVEMENT

As we have seen, reflective practice supports practitioners to develop and improve their practice. As such, it can contribute significantly to service development.

Whenever teams work on developing their reflective practice through reflective supervision and team meetings, service users report increased satisfaction – for example, see **Cosh** (2011).

Person-centred teams use reflective processes to inform their person-centred thinking and improve service delivery.

Reflective teams make an important contribution to the development of contemporary social care practice.

ENCOURAGING OTHERS TO BE REFLECTIVE

Much of contemporary social care practice focuses on supporting service users to learn and develop skills. For example:

▶ Early intervention and prevention services focus on enabling people to learn to address their own problems and situations

▶ Re-ablement services focus on enabling people to re-learn and maintain daily living skills

▶ Adults with learning disabilities are supported through extended opportunities and active support to learn and develop new skills

▶ Positive behaviour approaches involve supporting people to learn more about their behaviour

Recognising the important role that reflective practice has in developing practice, many social care workers and services are now encouraging service users to be reflective. This is shown in current qualification standards where, for example, standards on promoting positive behaviour refer to candidates supporting individuals to reflect on their behaviour.

Taking an approach which focuses on supporting individuals to reflect and to develop new skills is referred to as social pedagogy.

Social pedagogy has a long history in many European countries – particularly Denmark, France, Germany and the Netherlands. It has not really been practised in the UK, but is now a growing field of interest for the British Government.

> *Social pedagogy is an approach covering the whole lifespan of people, and with recognition to lifelong learning […] It has a person-centred value base and has become the preferred way of working with adults. Considering the need for improvement in adult services – the UK would benefit from conceiving social pedagogy in the broadest possible way and striving to implement it across all welfare services.*
> **ThemPra** 2009

The key concepts of social pedagogy can be summarised as:

▶ Promoting each person's wellbeing
▶ Encouraging reflection and learning
▶ Positive, empowering and professional relationships between the pedagogue and the person accessing the services
▶ Empowerment
▶ Reflective practice

Social pedagogy offers social care workers a way of describing the professional application of their skills. Social care workers are often involved in working with service users in an educational capacity to enable them to access opportunities and relate to others positively. Social pedagogy allows workers to examine how they use their skills to enable others to grow, develop and learn, and it is likely to continue to grow in the UK as a field of interest.

ETHICS AND REFLECTIVE PRACTICE

Social care can be very complex and a number of ethical dilemmas can arise. The values of social care provide a framework for ethical behaviour for social care workers. However, these values can come into conflict with others and at times might clash with each other. Issues such as confidentiality, privacy and risk taking can cause significant dilemmas in practice. As **Leathard and McLaren** (2007) state:

Ethical issues pose particular challenges for practitioners who are often deeply committed to the needs of service users and yet are confronted with systems and resources that do not adequately match their professional ambitions.

Loewenberg and Dolgoff (1996) are clear that there are no easy answers to ethical dilemmas and it is easy for practitioners who do not reflect to feel 'stuck'.

Ethical dilemmas can occur when workers have to choose between two competing demands or when every possible alternative in a situation would result in an undesirable outcome for an individual.

Maclean and Caffrey (2009) provide a framework for addressing ethical dilemmas that highlights the vital importance of reflective practice:

1 **Establish the facts**: what is the dilemma? What are the options? Who has a stake in the outcomes?
2 **Evaluate options from different perspectives**: which option will do most good or least harm? Will rights be respected? Which option helps all participate as fully as possible?
3 **Make a decision**: following reflection and wide consultation with others, make a decision
4 **Test the decision**: test the decision in wider discussion with other professionals – is this the same decision that others would reach in the same situation?

5   **Act**: action the decision

6   **Reflect**: reflect on the outcome. If necessary, work through the process again

EMOTIONAL INTELLIGENCE AND REFLECTIVE PRACTICE

Emotional intelligence is an important concept in leadership, management and business. It isn't yet particularly influential in social care practice. However, discussion about the relationship between theories of emotional intelligence and social care and social work have developed considerably in the last few years.

Emotional intelligence is about:

Being able to motivate oneself and persist in the face of frustrations, to control impulse and delay gratification, to regulate one's moods and keep distress from swamping the ability to think, to empathise and to hope.
Goleman 1996, cited in **Morrison** 2006

This definition makes the links between social care and emotional intelligence clear. Goleman could in fact be writing about social care work!

An essential aspect of emotional intelligence is the importance of reflection and self-awareness. So the two concepts are related in a number of ways.

Grant and Kinman (2009) believe that emotional intelligence and reflective ability together:

▷ *Foster wellbeing*
▷ *Enhance resilience to stress*
▷ *Create workers with an ability 'to fly'!*

WHY DO SOCIAL CARE WORKERS FIND REFLECTIVE PRACTICE CHALLENGING?

You are probably reading this book to help you develop your skills in reflective practice, so you might be able to answer this question yourself! However, there are a number of reasons why people might find reflection difficult. These include:

▶ Organisational constraints
▶ Time constraints
▶ Lack of clarity about reflective practice
▶ Difficulties with uncertainty
▶ Reflective practice can be painful and can create a confidence crisis for practitioners

CRITICAL REFLECTION AND THE ORGANISATION

The different forms of reflection and learning which we have explored so far demonstrate the significant impact that organisational culture can have on reflection. However, organisational policy, procedure and practice can make it difficult for practitioners to reflect. What has become known as 'conveyor belt social care' is all about outcomes and measuring 'how much' work has been completed. It can mean that the time needed for reflection is difficult to justify.

When Schön wrote about reflective practice in the 1980s, he recognised that organisations have a tendency to resist a professional's attempt to develop critically reflective practice. In more recent times, the move towards a managerialist approach to social care which focuses on audits and targets has magnified this organisational resistance.

Baldwin (2004) identified managerialist practice in social care work as a significant block to critically reflective practice.

TIME CONSTRAINTS

Reflective practice calls for time. One of the main complaints of social care workers relates to lack of time. Heavy workloads leave little, if any, time for reflection.

There is no doubt that social care work can be very hectic, but reflective practice is not about needing time to sit and think; it simply requires being thoughtful about what you are doing and considering the ways in which you can improve your practice. Time pressures are not a reason for failing to be reflective.

Many writers actually argue that reflective practice can, in fact, help where practitioners are short of time. For example, **Parton and O'Byrne** (2000:77) argue that *'reflexivity slows us down so that we can go faster'*.

REFLECTIVE PRACTICE AND UNCERTAINTY

Many workers lack clarity about what reflective practice actually is, which in itself creates uncertainty. Reflective practice also often creates uncertainty because reflection creates questions and yet more questions, to which it doesn't always provide the answers!

Reflection/uncertainty

This does not always sit comfortably in a world where managers want confident action and don't want to know that practitioners have unanswered questions. Social care staff often fear uncertainty and may avoid reflective practice because the uncertainty created can be a cause for concern. However, 'staying with the uncertainty' – **Ixer** (2000) – is an important aspect of being a truly reflective practitioner. This has been recognised in other professions for some time. For example, **Seedhouse** (1998) said that a 'willingness to work with uncertainty is at the heart of health care'.

BLAME CULTURE

It is widely recognised that there is a culture of blame in social care and social work. This can lead to social care workers being afraid to reflect on situations that didn't go so well, for fear of being 'blamed'. Recognising this, the **Social Care Institute for Excellence** (2005) states that:

The current culture of blame that presides … acts as a strong disincentive to organisational learning. The sector must shrug off its blame culture and start being constructive about learning from its mistakes.

This research report highlights that there are few opportunities for organisations to learn from 'near misses' and suggests that where learning occurs, it is located at the front line, often in supervision between practitioners and their managers. The Institute suggests that reflective practice should be encouraged and critical incident discussions should take place in order to effectively safeguard service users.

REFLECTIVE PRACTICE AS A THREAT

Practitioners can view reflective practice as a threat. Reflective practice can:

▶ Promote anxiety
▶ Create self-doubt
▶ Lead to mental blocks
▶ Focus on negatives, thus creating negativity and cynicism
▶ Weaken confidence
▶ Lead to self-absorption

Contemporary social care work is full of uncertainty and constant change. The creation of further uncertainty within the reflective process could destabilise a social care worker who is already struggling to keep things together. Whenever a social care worker feels that critical reflection is having a negative impact on them, they should discuss this with a trusted colleague or manager and possibly seek external support.

The fact is that the unknown is always there; reflective practice simply makes us more aware of it so that we can mull it over and consider our options. Avoiding reflective practice because of a fear of the unknown is not an option. It may simply be that social care staff need to have the safety net of a place they can discuss the reflective process and its results.

It is important to remember that critically reflective practice:

...should not produce cynics but confident people who can be committed to a point of view that is well-informed, rational and supported by relevant and valid material for that situation. These are the types of social care workers that the public deserve.
Brown and Rutter 2006:2

This section of the Pocket Guide has demonstrated that there are many answers to the question: 'Why is reflective practice important to social care work?'

Perhaps the most important, though, is that reflective practice helps social care workers to have a deeper understanding of themselves and their practice. This improves practice for the most important people engaged in social care: the users of the service.

It has also demonstrated that there are a number of barriers to reflective practice in contemporary social care. It is important for social care workers to be are aware of these barriers so that they can seek to address these in their practice.

HOW can social care workers apply and use reflective practice?

One of the criticisms social care workers often make about reflective practice is that it is not a concrete concept which they can directly apply to their practice. There are also a number of potential barriers to social care workers being reflective practitioners. This section of the Pocket Guide seeks to address how social care workers can directly apply reflective practice and find solutions to the barriers, by exploring issues such as:

▶ **What models of reflection have in common**
▶ **Planning for change and action**
▶ **Using feedback to inform practice**
▶ **Using supervision**
▶ **How to develop reflective writing**

WHAT DO THE MODELS HAVE IN COMMON?

Each of the models of reflective practice brings something different to the concept, which is why different practitioners find different models to be the most appealing to them. However, common themes and threads can be identified across the various models:

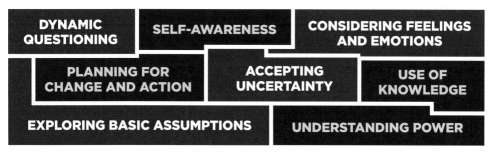

SELF-AWARENESS

Self-awareness is an essential aspect of reflective practice and of social care work generally. Each of us will have a different approach to a situation or a different impact on the situation because of who we are. It is therefore vital to 'know yourself', so that you can recognise the impact that you might be having on a situation. For example, **Burnard** (1992) talks about the vital importance of self-awareness for effective communication. He defines self-awareness as the 'process of getting to know your feelings, attitudes and values. It is also learning about the effect you have on others'.

Self-awareness and reflective practice are linked because:

▶ In your reflection you need to draw on an awareness of yourself and the impact you have

▶ Reflecting will enable you to develop a clearer self-awareness

DYNAMIC QUESTIONING

Reflective practice is fundamentally about exploration and inquiry. As such, it obviously involves asking various questions. The practical application of every model of reflection involves 'translating' the model into a series of questions to be explored. It is important to recognise, however, that reflective practice is not just about asking a question, finding an answer and moving on; indeed, it requires 'dynamic questioning'. This can mean:

▶ There is more than one 'answer' to the question
▶ Each question raises another question
▶ Questions prompt significant changes in the way a person looks at a situation

A reflective practitioner needs to be open to questions and not see the questions as a criticism of practice.

McClure (2002:5-6) suggests that reflective practice is based on a process of dynamic questioning and that the following 'reflective questions' can be used to assist in reflective practice – either in writing or in reflective discussions.

► What was I aiming for when I did that?

► What exactly did I do? (describing it precisely)

► Why did I choose that particular action?

► What theories/models/research informed my practice?

► What was I trying to achieve?

► What did I do next?

► What were the reasons for doing that?

► How successful was it?

► What criteria am I using to judge success?

► What alternatives were there?

► Could I have dealt with the situation any better?

► How would I do it differently next time?

► How do I feel about the whole experience?

- ► What knowledge/values/skills were demonstrated?
- ► How did the client feel about it?
- ► How do I know the client felt like that?
- ► What sense can I make of this in light of my past experience?
- ► Has this changed the way in which I will do things in the future?

REFLECTION AND REFLECTIVE PRACTICE

CONSIDERING FEELINGS AND EMOTIONS

All the models of reflective practice involve taking feelings and emotions into account. How you feel about a situation and how other people feel about a situation will have an impact on that situation and the possible outcomes – and reflective practice recognises this.

The impact of feelings and emotions on social care practice is often underestimated and rarely discussed. However, this is a vital area and one which we all have a responsibility to address.

If a carpenter is working with a piece of wood which he doesn't like, it won't have an impact on the wood (although you could argue it will have an impact on what he makes out of it!). However, social care workers work with people, and emotions have a huge impact on people.

A great deal is being written about contemporary social care and the feelings that are around at present. For example, **Samuel** (2010) says that fear, insecurity and anger are common feelings in social care at the moment. Certainly, there is a great deal of change taking place in social care at this point in time and change can create feelings of insecurity. It is vital that, as a social care worker, you are fully 'in touch' with your feelings and the impact these may have on your practice.

UNDERSTANDING POWER

Some of the models of reflective practice make specific reference to the importance of considering power as part of the reflective process – see, for example, **Fook** (2002). Power issues are vitally important in social care, but they are often overlooked in busy social care environments.

An essential aspect of being more reflective as a social care worker lies in being very aware of power in the situation. As part of the process of reflection, specifically thinking about power can bring about completely new ways of seeing things and improved ways of working. When reflecting on a situation, think about questions like:

▶ Who holds the power in this situation?
▶ How is this power expressed?
▶ Is anyone powerless in this situation? If so, who?
▶ Can I empower the service user in any way? If so, how?

USING KNOWLEDGE

This Pocket Guide illustrates that reflective practice is closely linked (often in a cycle) with other concepts. This is certainly true in terms of the links between knowledge and reflective practice, in that:

▶ An important part of the reflective process is about using the knowledge you have

▶ Reflection improves and extends knowledge, particularly the knowledge developed from practice, which is often referred to as practice wisdom

Very often the knowledge we use in social care comes from other areas, such as psychology or health care. As such, it needs to be 'translated' into the social care arena – and practitioners can do this through reflective practice.

To understand how reflective practice and knowledge match together, it can be useful to think of the knowledge we use as recipes for practice. You probably think that knowledge would inform everyone's practice in the same way. However, when different cooks use the same recipe, the dish often turns out differently. The result can depend on the skills of the cook, how the cook has adapted the recipe and whether they had all the ingredients easily to hand. The 'recipes' that social care workers use might be policies and procedures or theory and research; their practice, though, won't always turn out the same – this will depend on a whole variety of factors. It is therefore essential that social care workers reflect on the knowledge they are using and how they are using it. This will ensure that they provide consistently good care and support, and – to return to the example of recipes – that they obtain the best possible dish from the recipe they have. Reflecting on practice will help social care workers to improve the recipe.

EXPLORING BASIC ASSUMPTIONS

Reflective practice is about questioning and reconsidering assumptions. **Fook** (2004:59) said that '*reflective processes can potentially unearth any assumptions about anything* [...] *some crucial but hitherto deeply hidden assumptions may be uncovered.*'

PLANNING FOR CHANGE AND ACTION

There is no purpose to reflection for the sake of reflection. According to **Loewenberg and Dolgoff** (1996), practitioners who reflect with no outcome or commitment to action 'may find themselves in the same situation as the centipede who became incapable of moving about when it tried to understand how its legs worked'.

The final stage of reflection (whatever model the practitioner uses) must involve the social care worker thinking about what they have learnt as a result and how they might use that learning in the future. Questions might include, for example:

▶   What have I learnt from this?
▶   What might I do differently in future?
▶   How might I improve my practice?

It is vital that reflection always concludes with future planning. As **Atkins and Murphy** (1993) state:

For reflection to make a real difference to practice, it is important that the outcome includes a commitment to action. This may not necessarily involve acts which can be observed by others, but it is important that the individual makes a commitment of some kind on the basis of that learning. Action is the final stage of the reflective cycle.

KEEPING IT POSITIVE

Possibly because the word 'critical' appears so often in reference to reflective practice (eg critically reflective practice, critical thinking, critical incident analysis), the latter can be seen as the need to focus on events which didn't go so well.

The danger with this, of course, is that the spotlight is always on what went badly. Little is learnt from the positive outcomes and what went well.

It is, of course, vital that we learn the lessons from past mistakes and failures in systems but, in order to ensure effective and holistic reflection, practitioners really need to balance the issues on which they reflect so that reflection on positive practice also takes place. This is especially important to ensure that practitioners maintain the motivation for reflective practice.

GUIDANCE ON DEVELOPING REFLECTIVE PRACTICE

There are some specific things that social care workers can do to develop their skills in reflective practice. These include:

- Using feedback
- Using supervision
- Using a model to guide reflection
- Finding a critical friend
- Keeping a reflective journal
- Mind mapping

USING FEEDBACK

Accepting and receiving feedback is a vital skill which all social care workers need to have. It is widely accepted that being able to 'receive feedback gracefully is a career-enhancing skill which is greatly valued by employers', as stated by **King** (2007:1).

Social care workers might receive feedback in a range of ways (eg written and verbal) and from a variety of people (eg managers, other workers, service users, etc).

It is vital that feedback is used to inform the process of reflection.

▶ **Maintain an open attitude**: Don't be defensive or 'defend' yourself. If you find you are feeling defensive about a piece of feedback, remind yourself that a defensive reaction to feedback normally results from the latter being accurate!

- ▶ **Employ your active listening skills**: Listen actively, look at the person providing feedback and maintain an open body language.
- ▶ **Clarify the feedback**: Ask any questions you consider necessary in order to make sure you understand the feedback.
- ▶ **Recognise the giver of the feedback**: Providing feedback is not an easy task and the person who delivered it is likely to have put a great deal of thought into it. It takes a great deal of time and effort to provide thoughtful feedback and it is therefore advisable to thank the person who provided it – just something like 'You've really given me something to think about there. Thanks' not only demonstrates your commitment to learning, but also helps you to maintain that vital positive and open attitude.
- ▶ **Write down the feedback**: Try to write down as much you can remember of what was said as soon as possible. You will find this will assist with your reflection later.
- ▶ **Don't take criticism personally**: Feedback is a professional process. Recognise that part of being a professional is learning from how others perceive you.

▶ **Recognise learning**: Remember that simply because someone has picked up on an area of your practice which can be improved, this does not mean you are not a good social care worker. Even the very best worker can improve on some aspects of their practice.

▶ **Reflect**: If some aspects of the feedback puzzle you, take some time to reflect. How might the person's perception have been formed?

▶ **Focus**: Make sure that you are not distracted so that you can focus fully on what has been said. Stay 'in the moment' and try to understand truly the meaning behind the feedback. Try to avoid framing a response in your mind until you have heard all of the feedback.

▶ **Recognise your reactions**: Notice your own reactions and how the feedback is making you feel. Sometimes it helps to disassociate yourself partially and imagine you are a 'fly on the wall' witnessing feedback being given to someone else. This can help you to think the feedback through objectively rather than emotionally.

Rich (2009) suggests that in receiving feedback, people take either a negative (closed) style or a positive (open) style. The following table summarises this:

Negative/closed	Positive/open
Defensive: defends actions, objects to feedback	Open: listens without frequent interruptions or objections
Attacking: turns the table on the person providing feedback	Responsive: willing to truly 'hear' what is being said
Rejecting: refutes the accuracy or fairness of the feedback	Accepting: accepts the feedback without denial
Disrespectful: devalues the person giving the feedback	Respectful: recognises the value of the feedback
Closed: ignores the feedback	Engaged: interacts appropriately, seeking clarification where needed

Negative/closed	Positive/open
Inactive listening: makes no attempt to understand the meaning of the feedback	Active listening: listens attentively and tries to understand the meaning of the feedback
Rationalising: finds explanations for the feedback that dissolve personal responsibility	Thoughtful: tries to understand the personal behaviour that has led to the feedback
Superficial: listens and agrees but does not act on the feedback	Sincere: genuinely wants to make changes and learn

USING SUPERVISION

Social care workers report greatly varying experiences of supervision. Some practitioners rarely have supervision and when they do, it relates largely to meeting targets and discussing how much more work they can take on. Others report that they receive very good quality supervision, which is supportive and encourages their growth and professional development.

Current trends in policy are placing more emphasis on the importance of reflective supervision for social care workers. Good quality supervision should help you to explore your practice experiences, looking at what you found challenging and why, and helping you to consider how you might change and improve your practice in the future.

It is important to remember that promoting reflective practice within supervision is not just the responsibility of the supervisor. Social care practitioners need to take a reflective approach within supervision.

USING A MODEL TO GUIDE REFLECTION

Reflective practice is seen as an abstract concept and, since it is very often misunderstood as nothing more than thinking about practice, people can miss essential issues in their reflection. Using a specific model of reflective practice to guide your reflection can therefore be very useful.

The **WHAT?** section of this Pocket Guide outlined some of the main models of reflection used in social care and, when looking at them, you are likely to find some more appealing than others. It doesn't matter which model you use, but finding a model which you are comfortable with and using that to guide your reflection will certainly improve your skills in reflective practice.

CRITICAL FRIENDS

First introduced by **Stenhouse** (1975), the idea of a critical friend is based on finding a trusted listener who can act as an interested sounding board. Stenhouse introduced the idea for action research, but it has since been extended to support reflective practice. In the latter, the critical friend is a person who will listen to the practitioner and ask provocative questions to prompt deeper thinking. The critical friend might use a framework like the coaching conversation, or they might use a set of reflective questions such as those posed by **McClure** (2002) (see pages 84–85).

The idea of the critical friend is very important in social care work, where confidentiality limits the opportunities for discussion about working practices with others.

Research into the use of critical friends in medical education indicates that whilst having a critical friend is useful, it might be even more advantageous to be a critical friend to someone else in order to develop reflective practice skills – see **Dahlgren et al** (2006). It might therefore be useful for social care practitioners to pair up as critical friends to one another, which is what regularly happens informally in social work teams, particularly where practitioners are undertaking further study.

REFLECTIVE JOURNALS

Keeping a reflective journal can be very beneficial for developing skills in reflective practice. This is not something which is completed for academic purposes or which is going to be assessed – a reflective journal is something like a personal diary (used regularly). It doesn't need to be neat, and the spelling and grammar aren't important. The process of jotting things down reflectively is what is important.

According to **Richardson and Maltby** (1995), keeping a reflective journal and getting into the habit of writing in it regularly promotes the following qualities and skills, which are required for reflection:

- ▶ Open-mindedness
- ▶ Motivation
- ▶ Self-awareness
- ▶ Description and observation
- ▶ Critical analysis and problem solving
- ▶ Synthesis and evaluation

The benefits of keeping an unstructured reflective journal can be maximised by reviewing it regularly for recurring themes. This can really help in identifying learning needs, developing reflective practice and working towards a qualification.

MIND MAPPING

Mind mapping is a visual way of making notes using graphic, non-linear methods. Generally, a mind map will be very visual and will radiate out from a central point. Colour and images are often used so it can end up looking very much like a 'doodle', but it will contain the essential aspects of the note taking. This approach is based on the idea that large amounts of information can be recorded in a semi-structured way.

Alternative names for mind maps include: spider diagrams, webs or mind webs. In a way the use of this language demonstrates the fact that mind maps are carefully crafted and developed outwards from a central point. Using a mind map to develop reflection can be very useful.

Most mind maps are developed by hand, especially when they are being used for clarifying thoughts and further developing reflections. However, there are software programmes available for producing mind maps.

REFLECTIVE ACCOUNTS

Reflective accounts are commonly used in social care qualifications. Candidates may be asked to write reflective accounts about a specific incident or a particular area of practice. If a candidate is asked to write a reflective account, it is useful for them to identify a 'critical incident' to write about. **Fook and Askeland** (2007:522) refer to a critical incident as an example of practice which is 'in some way significant to the practitioner'. Sometimes candidates who are asked to write a reflective account produce a purely descriptive account of what happened; this is a 'narrative account' rather than a reflective account.

To demonstrate how knowledge, values and skills come together, it is important to write in a truly reflective way. The following models for reflective writing can assist with this.

The **Royal Melbourne Institute of Technology University** (2007) produced some useful guidance for their students around a **D-I-E-P** formula.

D	***Describe*** *objectively what happened: answer the question 'What did I see and hear?'*
I	***Interpret*** *the events: explain what you saw and heard (your new insights; your connections with other learning; your feelings; your hypotheses; your conclusions). Answer the question 'What might it mean?' or 'What was the reason why I did this activity?'*
E	***Evaluate*** *the effectiveness of what you observed/learned: make judgements clearly connected to observations made. Evaluation answers the question 'What is my opinion about what I observed or experienced? Why?'*
P	***Plan*** *how this information will be useful to you. What are your recommendations? (Be concrete.) Consider: 'In what ways might this learning experience serve me in my future?'*

Another model for reflective writing is for the writer to work through the cycle of experiential learning.

Concrete experience	What was the event?
Reflective observation	What are your personal thoughts and feelings about the experience?
Abstract conceptualisation	How can you draw on previous experiences and on your knowledge to help you 'make sense' of this experience?
Active experimentation	If this event were to occur again, what would you do differently? What additional knowledge do you need to gain?

Williams and Rutter (2007:141) offer the following model for reflective writing based on **Gibbs** (1988):

Description – *what happened?*
Feelings – *what were you thinking and feeling?*
Evaluation – *what was good and bad about the experience?*
Analysis – *what sense can you make of the situation?*
Conclusion – *what else could you have done?*
Action plan – *what did you learn? If the same situation arose again, what would you do?*

REFLECTIVE WRITING

Reflective writing can pose particular challenges to social care workers. They may well be very reflective in their practice, but often struggle to explore this in writing. However, as **Brown and Rutter** (2006:24) point out, *'It is not what you think or do but the way you write about it that is graded.'* So, like it or not, practitioners need to develop their skills in reflective writing.

BENEFITS OF REFLECTIVE WRITING

Jennifer Moon has written extensively on reflective writing (eg 1999, 2004, etc) and she is seen as a key expert in this area. She argues that there are many benefits to reflective writing, including:

- ▶ It forces us to give time to reflection
- ▶ It helps to slow the thought process down, thus helping us to sift material
- ▶ It makes us organise and clarify thoughts as we seek to structure the writing
- ▶ It gives us control over the material on which we reflect, as we choose what to include and what to omit
- ▶ It helps us to recognise whether we really understand something, as we have to try to explain it in words
- ▶ It records the moment, enabling us to step back and reflect further at a later stage

HOW TO WRITE REFLECTIVELY

▶ Using personal reflection, develop your argument, detail your points and then make links to things like theory and policy

▶ Go for depth

▶ Discuss rather than describe the incident

▶ Use a model of reflective practice to help provide a structure

▶ Show the use of 'self' – what unique impact did you have?

▶ Develop the writing from a review of regular journal entries

▶ Structure the writing

▶ Develop an early-stage draft and regularly review, edit and redevelop

▶ Don't forget to include reflection on outcomes

▶ Include reflection on what went well and on what didn't go so well

- ► Explore
- ► Question assumptions
- ► Develop breadth by exploring how a variety of knowledge has enhanced your reflection
- ► Include references to what you would do differently if you were in the same situation again
- ► Compare this situation with other experiences

MOVING FROM DESCRIPTIVE TO REFLECTIVE WRITING FOR ACADEMIC PURPOSES

Social care workers sometimes go on to higher level academic qualifications (such as foundation degrees) where they are required to write in a reflective style for academic purposes.

Hatton and Smith (1995) identified four levels of reflective writing for academic purposes:

Descriptive: The writer purely describes the event/practice.
Descriptive reflective: The writer gives a description of events. There is some deeper consideration but the language used in the writing is mostly associated with description. Different perspectives are not considered.

Dialogic reflective: The writer steps back from the situation, thus demonstrating they are mulling things over. They explore their own role and think about what they could have done differently. They analyse the situation, particularly making wider links, and different perspectives are considered.

Critically reflective: Together with all the elements of 'dialogic reflection', the writer shows also evidence of considering socio-political contexts. In social care this will involve giving consideration to anti-oppressive practice and power dynamics.

Writing which uses the critically reflective style will clearly receive higher marks.

TOP TIP!

In trying to develop reflective writing, it is worth sitting with the assignment and a few different coloured highlighter pens. Edit the work by highlighting anything which is purely descriptive in one colour, then where there is reflection use a different colour, where you discuss power issues use another colour, etc. You should find that the work becomes multi-coloured because if there are whole chunks of one colour that means that your work is not sufficiently critically reflective.

REFERENCES

Atkins, S and Murphy, K (1993) 'Reflection: a review of the literature' in *Journal of Advanced Nursing*, no 18, pp1188–1192

Baldwin, M (2004) 'Critical Reflection: Opportunities and Threats to Professional Learning and Service Development in Social Work Organisations', in **Gould, N and Baldwin, M** (eds) *Social Work, Critical Reflection and the Learning Organization*. (Aldershot) Ashgate Publishing Ltd

Biggs, J (1999) *Teaching for Quality Learning at University*. (Buckingham) Society for Research into Higher Development

Bolton, G (2001) *Reflective Practice*. (London) Sage

Borton, T (1970) *Reach, Teach and Touch*. (London) McGraw Hill

Boud, D, Keogh, R and Walker, D (1985) *Reflection: Turning Experience into Learning*. (London) Kogan Page

Brookfield, S (ed) (1988) *Training Educators of Adults: The Theory and Practice of Graduate Adult Education*. (New York) Routledge

Brown, K and Rutter, L (2006) *Critical Thinking for Social Work*. (Exeter) Learning Matters

Burnard, P (1992) *Effective Communication Skills*. (London) Chapman and Hall

Clouder, L (2000) 'Reflective Practice: Realising its Potential' in *Physiotherapy*, vol 86, no 10, pp517–521

Cosh, J (2011) 'Using video to boost reflective practice' in *Community Care*, 22.9.11, pp32–33

Dahlgren, L O, Eriksson, B E, Gyllenhammar, H, Korkeila, M and Saaf-Rothoff, A (2006) 'To be and to have a critical friend in medical teaching' in *Journal of Medical Education*, vol 40, no 1, pp5–6

Dean, J (1995) *What Makes a Profession?* Available online at www.allbusiness.com/whatmakesaprofession. Accessed 21.9.10

Dewey, J (1933) *How We Think: A Restatement of the Relation of Reflective Thinking to the Educative Process*. (Boston) DC Health

Eraut, M (1994) *Developing Professional Knowledge and Competence*. (London) Falmer

Fook, J (2002) *Social Work: Critical Theory and Practice*. (London) Sage

Fook, J (2004) 'Critical Reflection and Organizational Learning and Change: A Case Study' in **Gould, N and Baldwin, M** (eds) *Social Work, Critical Reflection and the Learning Organization*. (Aldershot) Ashgate

Fook, J and Askeland, A (2007) 'Challenges of critical reflection: nothing ventured, nothing gained' in *Social Work Education* 26 (5) pp520–533

Gibbs, G (1988) *Learning by Doing: A Guide to Teaching and Learning Methods*. (Oxford) Further Education Unit Oxford Polytechnic

Grant, L and Kinman, G (2009) *Developing Emotional Resilience in Social Work Students: Supporting Effective Reflective Practitioners*. Presentation at JSWEC Conference 2009

Greenaway, R (1995) *Powerful Learning Experiences in Management Learning and Development*. Available online at http://reviewing.co.uk/research/ple_abs.htm. Accessed 21.9.10

Hatton, N and Smith, D (1995) 'Reflection in Teacher Education: Towards definition and implementation' in *Teaching and Teacher Education*, vol 11, pp33–49

Honey, P and Mumford, A (1982) *Manual of Learning Styles*. (Maidenhead) Peter Honey Publications

Hooper, A and Parrot, A (2006) *Becoming a Professional through Reflective Practice*. (Leeds) NCA, BAAB.

Ixer, G (2000) 'Assessing Reflective Practice: New Research Findings' in *The Journal of Practice Teaching in Health and Social Work*, vol 2, no 3, pp19–27

Jarvis, P (1992) 'Reflective Practice and Nursing' in *Nurse Education Today*, vol 12, no 3, pp174–181

Johns, C (2000) *Becoming a Reflective Practitioner*. (Oxford) Blackwell

Killian, J and Todnem, G (1991) 'Reflective judgment concepts of justification and their relationship to age and education' in *Journal of Applied Developmental Psychology*, vol 2, no 2, pp89–116

King, J B (2007) *Receiving Feedback Gracefully is a Critical Career Skill*. Available online at www.sideroad.com/Career_Advice/receiving-feedback.html. Accessed 7.12.11

Kolb, D A (1984) *Experiential Learning: Experience as the Source of Learning and Development*. (New Jersey) Prentice Hall

Korthagen, F (2001) 'A Reflection on Reflection' in **Korthagen, F** (ed) *Linking Practice and Theory: The Pedagogy of Realistic Teacher Education*. (New Jersey) Lawrence Erlbaum Associates

Leathard, A and McLaren, S (eds) (2007) *Ethics: Contemporary Challenges in Health and Social Care*. (Bristol) Policy Press

Loewenberg, F and Dogloff, R (1996) 'Ethical Choices in the Helping Professions' in **Loewenberg, F and Dogloff, R** *Ethical Decisions for Social Work Practice*. 5th edition. (Illinois) Peacock

Maclean, S and Caffrey, B (2009) *Developing a Practice Learning Curriculum: A Guide for Practice Educators*. (Rugeley) Kirwin Maclean Associates Ltd

Marton, S and Saljo, R (1976) 'On Qualitative Differences in Learning: 1. Outcome and Process' in *British Journal of Educational Psychology*, vol 46, pp4–11

Mezirow, J (ed) (2000) *Learning as Transformation: Critical Perspectives on a Theory in Progress*. (San Francisco) Jossey Bass

McClure, P (2002) *Reflection on Practice. Making Practice-Based Learning Work*. (Ulster) University of Ulster

Moon, J (1999) *Learning Journals: A Handbook for Academics, Students and Professional Development*. (London) Kogan Page

Moon, J (2004) *A Handbook of Reflective and Experiential Learning*. (London) Routledge Farmer

Morrison, T (2006) 'Emotional Intelligence, Emotion and Social Work: Context, Characteristics, Complications and Contribution' in *British Journal of Social Work*, vol 37, no 2, pp245–263

Parton, N and O'Bryne, P (2000) *Constructive Social Work: Towards a New Practice*. (Hampshire) Macmillan Press Ltd

Reagan, T G, Case, C W and Brubacher, J W (2000) *Becoming a Reflective Educator: How to Build a Culture of Inquiry in Schools* (2nd ed). (California) Corwin

Reid, B (1993) 'But We're Doing it Already! Exploring a Response to the Concept of Reflective Practice in Order to Improve its Facilitation' in *Nurse Education Today*, vol 13, no 4, pp305–309

Rich, P (2009) *Giving and Receiving Feedback*. Available online at
www.selfhelpmagazine.com/articles/growth/feedback.html.
Accessed 10.9.09

Richardson, G and Maltby, H (1995) 'Reflection on Practice:
Enhancing Student Learning' in *Journal of Advanced Nursing*, vol 22,
no 2, pp235–242

RMIT University Study and Learning Centre (2007) *Reflective Journal Help*.
Available online at: www.dlsweb.rmit.edu.au/lsu/content2_
AssessmentTasks/assess_pdf/Reflective%20journal.pdf. Accessed 12.1.08

Roth, R (1989) 'Preparing the reflective practitioner: Transforming the
apprentice through the dialectic' in *Journal of Teacher Education*,
vol 40, no 2, pp31–35

Samuel, M (2010) *Wielding the Axe*. Community Care 11.11.2010

Schön, D (1983) *The Reflective Practitioner: How Professionals Think in Action*.
(London) Temple Smith

Seedhouse, D (1998) *Ethics: the heart of health care*. (Chichester) Wiley

Smith, S and Karban, K (2006) *Developing Critical Reflection within an Interpersonal Learning Programme.* (Leeds Metropolitan University). Available online at www.leeds.ac.uk/medicine/meu/lifelong06/P_SueSmith_KateKarban.pdf. Accessed 6.2.10

Smyth, J (1989) 'Developing and sustaining critical reflection in teacher education' in *Journal of Teacher Education*, vol 40, no 2, pp2–9

Social Care Institute for Excellence (2005) *SCIE Report 6: Managing risks and minimising mistakes in services to children and families.* (London) SCIE

Stenhouse, L (1975) *An Introduction to Curriculum Research and Development.* (London) Heinemann

ThemPra Social Pedagogy Community Interest Society (2009) *Social Pedagogy: Theory meets Practice.* Available online at www.social-pedagogy.co.uk/concepts.htm. Accessed 19.1.10

University of York (2000) *Facts, Feelings and Feedback. A Collaborative Model for Direct Observation.* (York) University of York

Williams, S and Rutter, A (2007) *Enabling and Assessing Work Based Learning for Social Work: Supporting the Development of Professional Practice.* (Birmingham) Learn to Care

City & Guilds is the UK's leading provider of vocational qualifications, offering over 500 awards across a wide range of industries, and progressing from entry level to the highest levels of professional achievement. With over 8,500 centres in 100 countries, City & Guilds is recognised by employers worldwide.

Publications

For information about, or to order support materials, contact the Publishing department on +44 (0)20 7294 4113 or learningmaterials@cityandguilds.com. More information about the materials is available at www.cityandguilds.com/publications. For further copies of this Pocket Guide, or other qualification documentation, contact our Publication Sales department on +44 (0)20 7294 2850 or by fax +44 (0)20 7294 3387.

Every effort has been made to ensure that the information contained in this publication is true and correct at the time of going to press. However, City & Guilds' products and services are subject to continuous development and improvement and the right is reserved to change products and services from time to time. City & Guilds cannot accept liability for loss or damage arising from the use of information in this publication.